The Kahlil Gibran Diary for 1973

THE KAHLIL GIBRAN
DIARY FOR 1973

ALFRED A. KNOPF

NEW YORK

ISBN: 0-394-48268-9, blue binding; 0-394-48269-7, red; 0-394-48270-0, ivory.

This diary contains selections from the following works by Kahlil Gibran,
published by Alfred A. Knopf, Inc.:

The Madman: Copyright 1918 by Kahlil Gibran. Copyright renewed 1946 by Comité National
de Gibran. (*Weeks of January 29, May 21, July 16, August 27, and December 17*)

The Forerunner: Copyright 1920 by Kahlil Gibran. Copyright renewed 1948 by Mary G. Gibran
and William Saxe. (*Weeks of March 26, July 30, October 8, and December 3*)

The Prophet: Copyright 1923 by Kahlil Gibran. Copyright renewed 1951 by Mary G. Gibran
and William Saxe. (*Weeks of January 15, March 12, April 30, June 25, October 29, December
24, and December 31*)

Sand and Foam: Copyright 1926 by Kahlil Gibran. Copyright renewed 1954 by Mary G. Gibran
and William Saxe. (*Weeks of January 22, May 14, July 2, August 6, September 24, and
November 5*)

Jesus the Son of Man: Copyright 1928 by Kahlil Gibran. Copyright renewed 1956 by Mary G.
Gibran and William Saxe. (*Weeks of March 5, April 16, and June 11*)

The Earth Gods: Copyright 1931 by Kahlil Gibran. Copyright renewed 1959 by Mary G. Gibran
and William Saxe. (*Weeks of May 7 and October 1*)

The Wanderer: Copyright 1932 by Alfred A. Knopf, Inc. Copyright renewed 1960 by Mary K.
Gibran. (*Weeks of April 9, June 18, and October 22*)

The Garden of the Prophet: Copyright 1933 by Alfred A. Knopf, Inc. Copyright renewed 1961
by Mary K. Gibran. (*Weeks of February 19 and September 3*)

Prose Poems: Copyright 1934 by Alfred A. Knopf, Inc. Copyright renewed 1962 by Alfred A.
Knopf, Inc. (*Weeks of February 5 and July 9*)

Spirits Rebellious: Copyright 1948 by Alfred A. Knopf, Inc. (*Weeks of March 19, May 28, and
November 26*)

A Tear and A Smile: Copyright 1950 by Alfred A. Knopf, Inc. (*Weeks of January 8, February 12,
April 2, August 13, September 17, November 12, and December 10*)

There are also selections from *Beloved Prophet*, The Love Letters of Kahlil Gibran and Mary
Haskell and Her Private Journal, Edited and Arranged by Virginia Hilu. Copyright © 1972
by Alfred A. Knopf, Inc. (*Weeks of January 1, February 26, April 23, June 4, July 23,
August 20, September 10, October 15, and November 19*)

Manufactured in the United States of America

FIRST EDITION

Frontispiece: Gibran at 25, from an oil painting by Yusef Hoyiek

This diary belongs to

_____

JANUARY

Mon	Tue	Wed	Thu	Fri	Sat	Sun
1	2	3	4	5	6	7
8	9	10	11	12	13	14
15	16	17	18	19	20	21
22	23	24	25	26	27	28
29	30	31				

MAY

Mon	Tue	Wed	Thu	Fri	Sat	Sun
	1	2	3	4	5	6
7	8	9	10	11	12	13
14	15	16	17	18	19	20
21	22	23	24	25	26	27
28	29	30	31			

FEBRUARY

Mon	Tue	Wed	Thu	Fri	Sat	Sun
			1	2	3	4
5	6	7	8	9	10	11
12	13	14	15	16	17	18
19	20	21	22	23	24	25
26	27	28				

JUNE

Mon	Tue	Wed	Thu	Fri	Sat	Sun
				1	2	3
4	5	6	7	8	9	10
11	12	13	14	15	16	17
18	19	20	21	22	23	24
25	26	27	28	29	30	

MARCH

Mon	Tue	Wed	Thu	Fri	Sat	Sun
			1	2	3	4
5	6	7	8	9	10	11
12	13	14	15	16	17	18
19	20	21	22	23	24	25
26	27	28	29	30	31	

JULY

Mon	Tue	Wed	Thu	Fri	Sat	Sun
						1
2	3	4	5	6	7	8
9	10	11	12	13	14	15
16	17	18	19	20	21	22
23	24	25	26	27	28	29
30	31					

APRIL

Mon	Tue	Wed	Thu	Fri	Sat	Sun
						1
2	3	4	5	6	7	8
9	10	11	12	13	14	15
16	17	18	19	20	21	22
23	24	25	26	27	28	29
30						

AUGUST

Mon	Tue	Wed	Thu	Fri	Sat	Sun
		1	2	3	4	5
6	7	8	9	10	11	12
13	14	15	16	17	18	19
20	21	22	23	24	25	26
27	28	29	30	31		

SEPTEMBER

Mon	Tue	Wed	Thu	Fri	Sat	Sun
					1	2
3	4	5	6	7	8	9
10	11	12	13	14	15	16
17	18	19	20	21	22	23
24	25	26	27	28	29	30

OCTOBER

Mon	Tue	Wed	Thu	Fri	Sat	Sun
1	2	3	4	5	6	7
8	9	10	11	12	13	14
15	16	17	18	19	20	21
22	23	24	25	26	27	28
29	30	31				

NOVEMBER

Mon	Tue	Wed	Thu	Fri	Sat	Sun
			1	2	3	4
5	6	7	8	9	10	11
12	13	14	15	16	17	18
19	20	21	22	23	24	25
26	27	28	29	30		

DECEMBER

Mon	Tue	Wed	Thu	Fri	Sat	Sun
					1	2
3	4	5	6	7	8	9
10	11	12	13	14	15	16
17	18	19	20	21	22	23
24	25	26	27	28	29	30
31						

New Year's Day: January 1st

Kahlil Gibran's Birthday: January 6th (1883)

Lincoln's Birthday: February 12th

St. Valentine's Day: February 14th

Washington's Birthday: February 19th

Ash Wednesday: March 7th

St. Patrick's Day: March 17th

Palm Sunday: April 15th

Passover: April 17th

Good Friday: April 20th

Easter Sunday: April 22nd

Mother's Day: May 13th

Memorial Day: May 28th

Father's Day: June 17th

Independence Day: July 4th

Labor Day: September 3rd

Rosh Hashanah: September 27th

Yom Kippur: October 6th

Columbus Day: October 8th

Veterans Day: October 22nd

Halloween: October 31st

Election Day: November 6th

Thanksgiving Day: November 22nd

Channukah: December 20th

Christmas Day: December 25th

Hope

I cannot say much now about that which fills my heart and soul. I feel like a seeded field in midwinter, and I know that spring is coming. My brooks will run and the little life that sleeps in me will rise to the surface when called.

Monday

Tuesday

Wednesday

Thursday

Friday

The week of January 1st *to* January 7th

Saturday

Sunday

The *week of* January 8th *to* January 14th

Monday

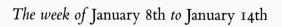

Tuesday

Wednesday

The week of January 8th *to* January 14th

Thursday

Friday

The *week of* January 8th *to* January 14th

The Peace and Passion of The Lord

Among the hills, when you sit in the cool shade of the white poplars, sharing the peace and serenity of distant fields and meadows—then let your heart say in silence, "God rests in reason."

And when the storm comes, and the mighty wind shakes the forest, and thunder and lightning proclaim the majesty of the sky—then let your heart say in awe, "God moves in passion."

And since you are a breath in God's sphere, and a leaf in God's forest, you too should rest in reason and move in passion.

Monday

Tuesday

Wednesday

Thursday

Friday

Saturday

Sunday

Men and Angels

The first thought of God was an angel.
The first word of God was a man.

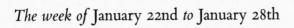

The *week of* January 22nd *to* January 28th

Monday

Tuesday

Wednesday

The week of January 22nd *to* January 28th

Thursday

Friday

urday

nday

The Three Ants

Three ants met on the nose of a man who was lying asleep in the sun. And after they had saluted one another, each according to the custom of his tribe, they stood there conversing.

The first ant said, "These hills and plains are the most barren I have known. I have searched all day for a grain of some sort, and there is none to be found."

Said the second ant, "I too have found nothing, though I have visited every nook and glade. This is, I believe, what my people call the soft, moving land where nothing grows."

Then the third ant raised his head and said, "My friends, we are standing now on the nose of the Supreme Ant, the mighty and infinite Ant, whose body is so great that we cannot see it, whose shadow is so vast that we cannot trace it, whose voice is so loud that we cannot hear it; and He is omnipresent."

When the third ant spoke thus the other ants looked at each other and laughed.

At that moment the man moved and in his sleep raised his hand and scratched his nose, and the three ants were crushed.

The *week of* January 29th *to* February 4th

Thursday

Friday

urday

nday

Not My Will but Thine Be Done

My soul counseled me and instructed me to see that the
    light which I carry is not my light,
That my song was not created within me;
For though I travel with the light, I am not the light,
And though I am a lute fastened with strings,
I am not the lute player.

Monday

Tuesday

Wednesday

The *week of* February 5th *to* February 11th

Thursday

Friday

The *week of* February 5th *to* February 11th

Saturday

Sunday

Monday

Tuesday

Wednesday

The *week of* February 12th *to* February 18th

Thursday

Friday

The week of February 12th *to* February 18th

Saturday

Sunday

A Land of Sorrow

My friends and my roadfellows, pity the nation that is full of beliefs and empty of religion.

Pity the nation that wears a cloth it does not weave, eats a bread it does not harvest, and drinks a wine that flows not from its own wine-press.

Pity the nation that acclaims the bully as hero, and that deems the glittering conqueror bountiful.

Pity a nation that despises a passion in its dream, yet submits in its awakening.

Pity the nation that raises not its voice save when it walks in a funeral, boasts not except among its ruins, and will rebel not save when its neck is laid between the sword and the block.

Pity the nation whose statesman is a fox, whose philosopher is a juggler, and whose art is the art of patching and mimicking.

Pity the nation that welcomes its new ruler with trumpetings, and farewells him with hootings, only to welcome another with trumpetings again.

Pity the nation whose sages are dumb with years and whose strong men are yet in the cradle.

Pity the nation divided into fragments, each fragment deeming itself a nation.

The *week of* February 19th *to* February 25th

Monday

Tuesday

Wednesday

The *week of* February 19th *to* February 25th

Thursday

Friday

Saturday

Sunday

Memory

Everyone has experienced that truth: that love, like a running brook, is disregarded, taken for granted; but when the brook freezes over, then people begin to remember how it was when it ran, and they want it to run again.

The week of February 26th to March 4th

Monday

Tuesday

Wednesday

The *week of* February 26th *to* March 4th

Thursday

Friday

The week of February 26th *to* March 4th

Saturday

Sunday

Our Father

Our Father in earth and heaven, sacred is Thy name.
Thy will be done with us, even as in space.
Give us of Thy bread sufficient for the day.
In Thy compassion forgive us and enlarge us to forgive
    one another.
Guide us towards Thee and stretch down Thy hand to us
    in darkness.
For Thine is the kingdom, and in Thee is our power and
    our fulfillment.

The week of March 5th to March 11th

Monday

Tuesday

Wednesday

Thursday

Friday

Saturday

Sunday

Crime and Punishment

Then one of the judges of the city stood forth and said, "Speak to us of Crime and Punishment."

And he answered, saying:

"It is when your spirit goes wandering upon the wind,

"That you, alone and unguarded, commit a wrong unto others and therefore unto yourself.

"And for that wrong committed must you knock and wait a while unheeded at the gate of the blessed."

The *week of* March 12th *to* March 18th

Monday

Tuesday

Wednesday

The week of March 12th *to* March 18th

Thursday

Friday

Saturday

Sunday

Rude Awakening

Unhappy is the man who loves a maiden and takes her for his lifemate, pouring out at her feet the sweat of his brow and his heart's blood, placing in her hands the fruits of his labor and the yield of his toil, and then learns, suddenly, that her heart, which he sought to buy with exertion by day and watchfulness by night, is given as a gift to another that he may take pleasure in its hidden things and rejoice in the secrets of its love.

Unhappy the woman who awakens from youth's ignorance to find herself in the house of a man who overwhelms her with his gifts and riches and clothes her with generosity and kindliness, yet is not able to touch her heart with the living flame of love nor yet satisfy her spirit with the divine wine that God makes to flow from a man's eyes into a woman's heart.

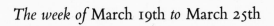

The *week of* March 19th *to* March 25th

Monday

Tuesday

Wednesday

The *week of* March 19th *to* March 25th

Thursday

Friday

The week of March 19th *to* March 25th

rday

day

Monday

Tuesday

Wednesday

Thursday

Friday

The week of March 26th *to* April 1st

turday

nday

The First Kiss

. . . A word uttered by four lips making the heart a throne,
and love a sovereign, and fulfillment a crown.

The *week of* April 2nd *to* April 8th

The *week of* April 2nd *to* April 8th

Thursday

Friday

The week of April 2nd *to* April 8th

Saturday

Sunday

❖{ *Body and Soul* }❖

A man and a woman sat by a window that opened upon Spring. They sat close one unto the other. And the woman said, "I love you. You are handsome, and you are rich, and you are always well-attired."

And the man said, "I love you. You are a beautiful thought, a thing too apart to hold in the hand, and a song in my dreaming."

But the woman turned from him in anger, and she said, "Sir, please leave me now. I am not a thought, and I am not a thing that passes in your dreams. I am a woman. I would have you desire me, a wife, and the mother of unborn children."

And they parted.

And the man was saying in his heart, "Behold another dream is even now turned into the mist."

And the woman was saying, "Well, what of a man who turns me into a mist and a dream?"

The *week of* April 9th *to* April 15th

Monday

Tuesday

Wednesday

The week of April 9th to April 15th

Thursday

Friday

The Son of Man

Jesus the Nazarene was born and reared like ourselves; His mother and father were like our parents, and He was a man.

But the Christ, the Word, who was in the beginning, the Spirit who would have us live our fuller life, came unto Jesus and was with Him.

And the Spirit was the versèd hand of the Lord, and Jesus was the harp.

The Spirit was the psalm, and Jesus the tune thereof.

And Jesus, the Man of Nazareth, was the host and the mouthpiece of the Christ, who walked with us in the sun and who called us His friends.

In those days the hills of Galilee and her valleys heard naught but His voice. And I was a youth then, and trod in His path and pursued His footprints.

I pursued His footprints and trod in His path, to hear the words of the Christ from the lips of Jesus of Galilee.

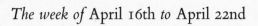

The week of April 16th *to* April 22nd

Monday

Tuesday

Wednesday

The week of April 16th to April 22nd

Thursday

Friday

The week of April 16th *to* April 22nd

Saturday

Sunday

Spring

When spring is dancing among the hills one should not stay in a little dark corner.

The week of April 23rd to April 29th

Monday

Tuesday

Wednesday

Thursday

Friday

The week of April 23rd *to* April 29th

Saturday

Sunday

Companionship

Give your hearts, but not into each other's keeping.
For only the hand of Life can contain your hearts.
And stand together yet not too near together:
For the pillars of the temple stand apart,
And the oak tree and the cypress grow not in each other's
    shadow.

The week of April 30th to May 6th

Monday

Tuesday

Wednesday

The week of April 30th to May 6th

Thursday

Friday

The week of April 30th *to* May 6th

Saturday

Sunday

The week of May 7th to May 13th

Monday

Tuesday

Wednesday

The *week of* May 7th *to* May 13th

Thursday

Friday

The week of May 7th *to* May 13th

aturday

unday

A Question of Viewpoint

A woman protested, saying, "Of course it was a righteous war. My son fell in it."

The week of May 14th to May 20th

Monday

Tuesday

Wednesday

The week of May 14th to May 20th

Thursday

Friday

The week of May 14th to May 20th

aturday

mday

The New Pleasure

Last night I invented a new pleasure, and as I was giving it the first trial an angel and a devil came rushing toward my house. They met at my door and fought with each other over my newly created pleasure; the one crying, "It is a sin!"—the other, "It is a virtue!"

The week of May 21st to May 27th

Monday

Tuesday

Wednesday

Thursday

Friday

The week of May 21st to May 27th

Saturday

Sunday

⊹{ *Happiness Now* }⊹

Without worth are the teachings and beliefs that make
man wretched in his existence. And false are the feelings
that lead him only to sorrow and despair. For it is a duty
that man has to be happy in the world and know the roads
to happiness and preach in its name wheresoever he be.
Who sees not the kingdom of heaven in this world will
not see it in the hereafter. We come not to this world as
outcasts, but as ignorant children, that we may learn from
life's beauties and secrets the worship of the everlasting and
universal spirit and the search after the hidden things of
the soul.

The week of May 28th to June 3rd

Monday

Tuesday

Wednesday

Thursday

Friday

The week of May 28th *to* June 3rd

aturday

unday

Form and Content

What a man wants to say determines how he says it. If he has a vision of life, he is always putting that vision before us—in different forms. We unconsciously contradict ourselves when we say we like a man's style and not his ideas. Style and ideas are one.

Monday

Tuesday

Wednesday

The week of June 4th *to* June 10th

Thursday

Friday

The week of June 4th to June 10th

Saturday

Sunday

The week of June 11th to June 17th

Monday

Tuesday

Wednesday

The *week of* June 11th *to* June 17th

The week of June 11th to June 17th

Saturday

Sunday

The Shadow

Upon a June day the grass said to the shadow of an elm tree, "You move to right and left over-often, and you disturb my peace."

And the shadow answered and said, "Not I, not I. Look skyward. There is a tree that moves in the wind to the east and to the west, between the sun and the earth."

And the grass looked up, and for the first time beheld the tree. And it said in its heart, "Why, behold, there is a larger grass than myself."

And the grass was silent.

The *week of* June 18th *to* June 24th

The *week of* June 18th *to* June 24th

Thursday

Friday

urday

nday

The Blame Is Shared

And this also, though the word lie heavy upon your hearts:
    The murdered is not unaccountable for his own murder,
    And the robbed is not blameless in being robbed.
    The righteous is not innocent of the deeds of the wicked,
    And the white-handed is not clean in the doings of the felon.
    Yea, the guilty is oftentimes the victim of the injured,
    And still more often the condemned is the burden bearer for the guiltless and unblamed.
    You cannot separate the just from the unjust and the good from the wicked;
    For they stand together before the face of the sun even as the black thread and the white are woven together.
    And when the black thread breaks, the weaver shall look into the whole cloth, and he shall examine the loom also.

The *week of* June 25th *to* July 1st

Monday

Tuesday

Wednesday

Thursday

Friday

The week of June 25th to July 1st

Saturday

Sunday

Trees

Trees are poems that the earth writes upon the sky. We fell them down and turn them into paper that we may record our emptiness.

The week of July 2nd to July 8th
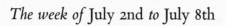

Monday

Tuesday

Wednesday

Thursday

Friday

Saturday

Sunday

What Is Love?

And what is this that we call love?
Tell me, what is this mystic secret hiding behind the sem-
    blance of our life,
And living in the heart of our existence?
What is this vast release coming as a cause to all effects,
    and as an effect unto all causes?
What is this quickening that gathers death and life and
    from them creates a dream
More strange than life, and deeper far than death?
Tell me, my brothers, tell me, which of you would not
    awake from this sleep of life
When your spirit feels the touch of love's white fingers?

The week of July 9th to July 15th

Monday

Tuesday

Wednesday

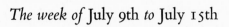

The week of July 9th to July 15th

Thursday

Friday

Saturday

Sunday

The week of July 16th *to* July 22nd

Monday

Tuesday

Wednesday

The week of July 16th *to* July 22nd

Thursday

Friday

The week of July 16th *to* July 22nd

Saturday

Sunday

Knowledge and Beauty

I now want to know all things under the sun, and the moon, too. For all things are beautiful in themselves, and become more beautiful when known to man. Knowledge is Life with wings.

The week of July 23rd to July 29th

Monday

Tuesday

Wednesday

The week of July 23rd to July 29th

Thursday

Friday

The week of July 23rd *to* July 29th

aturday

unday

⚜{ *Values* }⚜

Once a man unearthed in his field a marble statue of great beauty. And he took it to a collector who loved all beautiful things and offered it to him for sale, and the collector bought it for a large price. And they parted.

And as the man walked home with his money he thought, and he said to himself, "How much life this money means! How can anyone give all this for a dead carved stone buried and undreamed of in the earth for a thousand years?"

And now the collector was looking at his statue, and he was thinking, and he said to himself, "What beauty! What life! The dream of what a soul!—and fresh with the sweet sleep of a thousand years. How can anyone give all this for money, dead and dreamless?"

The *week of* July 30th *to* August 5th

Tuesday

Wednesday

The week of July 30th to August 5th

Thursday

Friday

The week of July 30th *to* August 5th

{Sadness}

Sadness is but a wall between two gardens.

The week of August 6th *to* August 12th

The *week of* August 6th *to* August 12th

Thursday

Friday

The week of August 6th *to* August 12th

Saturday

Sunday

❧ *Song of the Flower* ❧

I am a word uttered by Nature,
Then taken back
And hidden in her heart,
And a second time uttered.
I am a star fallen from the blue sky
Upon a green carpet.

I am a daughter of the elements:
Carried in Winter,
Born of Spring,
Reared by Summer;
And Autumn lays me to rest.

I am a gift to lovers
And a nuptial crown.
I am the last offering of the quick to the dead.

With morning's coming
I and the breeze together
Proclaim the light.
At even the birds and I bid it farewell.

I sway upon the plains
And adorn them.
I breathe my fragrance to the air.
I embrace slumber,
And the manifold eyes of night look long upon me.
I seek awakening to look on the single eye of day.

I drink of the dew's intoxication
And hearken to the blackbird's song.
I dance to the rhythm of the grasses shouting;
I look ever heavenward to see the light,
Not to behold therein my image.
This is a wisdom man has not learned yet.

The *week of* August 13th *to* August 19th

Monday

Tuesday

Wednesday

The *week* of August 13th *to* August 19th

Thursday

Friday

The week of August 13th *to* August 19th

Saturday

Sunday

The Fruit of Past Actions

Human consciousness is the fruit of the infinite past. The infinite future will make it ripe but it will never change its properties.

The *week of* August 20th *to* August 26th

Monday

Tuesday

Wednesday

The *week of* August 20th *to* August 26th

Thursday

Friday

The week of August 20th *to* August 26th

Saturday

Sunday

The *week of* August 27th *to* September 2nd

Monday

Tuesday

Wednesday

The week of August 27th to September 2nd

Thursday

Friday

The week of August 27th *to* September 2nd

Saturday

Sunday

❧ *Ugliness* ❧

And Sarkis, he who was the half-doubter, spoke and said: "And what of ugliness, Master? You speak never of ugliness."

And Almustafa answered him, and there was a whip in his words, and he said: "My friend, what man shall call you inhospitable if he shall pass by your house, yet would not knock at your door?

"And who shall deem you deaf and unmindful if he shall speak to you in a strange tongue of which you understand nothing?

"Is it not that which you have never striven to reach, into whose heart you have never desired to enter, that you deem ugliness?

"If ugliness is aught, indeed, it is but the scales upon our eyes, and the wax filling our ears.

"Call nothing ugly, my friend, save the fear of a soul in the presence of its own memories."

The week of September 3rd *to* September 9th

Monday

Tuesday

Wednesday

Thursday

Friday

The *week* *of* September 3rd *to* September 9th

Saturday

Sunday

Union

No human relation gives one possession in another—every two souls are absolutely different. In friendship or in love, the two side by side raise hands together to find what one cannot reach alone.

Monday

Tuesday

Wednesday

Thursday

Friday

The week of September 10th *to* September 16th

⊹{ *The Abode of Happiness* }⊹

Then my heart spoke to the daughter of Love and said: "Where is contentment, O Love? I had heard that it shared with you this dwelling." And she answered: "Contentment is away preaching in the city, where is corruption and greed; we are not in need of it in this place. Happiness desires not contentment, for happiness is naught but a longing that union embraces; contentment is a diversion conquered by forgetfulness. The immortal soul is not contented, for it is ever desiring of perfection; and perfection is the Infinite."

The week of September 17th *to* September 23rd

Monday

Tuesday

Wednesday

Thursday

Friday

Place Is All-Important

Said a gracious wolf to a simple sheep, "Will you not honor our house with a visit?"

And the sheep answered: "We would have been honored to visit your house if it were not in your stomach."

Monday

Tuesday

Wednesday

The *week of* September 24th *to* September 30th

Thursday

Friday

urday

nday

sday

sday

Inesday

Thursday

Friday

urday

nday

·{ *Other Seas* }·

A fish said to another fish, "Above this sea of ours there
is another sea, with creatures swimming in it—and they
live there even as we live here."

The fish replied, "Pure fancy! Pure fancy! When you
know that everything that leaves our sea by even an inch,
and stays out of it, dies. What proof have you of other
lives in other seas?"

Monday

Tuesday

Wednesday

Thursday

Friday

Saturday

Sunday

Growing in Silence

Silence is painful; but in silence things take form, and we must wait and watch. In us, in our secret depth, lies the knowing element which sees and hears that which we do not see nor hear. All our perceptions, all the things we have done, all that we are today, dwelt once in that knowing, silent depth, that treasure chamber in the soul. And we are more than we think. We are more than we know. That which is more than we think and know is always seeking and adding to itself while we are doing nothing—or think we are doing nothing. But to be conscious of what is going on in our depth is to help it along. When sub-consciousness becomes consciousness, the seeds in our winter-clad selves turn to flowers, and the silent life in us sings with all its might.

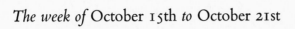

The *week of* October 15th *to* October 21st

Monday

Tuesday

Wednesday

Thursday

Friday

Saturday

Sunday

Peace and War

Three dogs were basking in the sun and conversing.

The first dog said dreamily, "It is indeed wondrous to be living in this day of dogdom. Consider the ease with which we travel under the sea, upon the earth, and even in the sky. And meditate for a moment upon the inventions brought forth for the comfort of dogs, even for our eyes and ears and noses."

And the second dog spoke and he said, "We are more heedful of the arts. We bark at the moon more rhythmically than did our forefathers. And when we gaze at ourselves in the water we see that our features are clearer than the features of yesterday."

Then the third dog spoke and said, "But what interests me most and beguiles my mind is the tranquil understanding existing between dogdoms."

At that very moment they looked, and lo, the dog-catcher was approaching.

The three dogs sprang up and scampered down the street; and as they ran the third dog said,

"For God's sake, run for your lives. Civilization is after us."

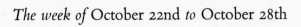

The week of October 22nd *to* October 28th

Monday

Tuesday

Wednesday

Thursday

Friday

The *week of* October 22nd *to* October 28th

Saturday

Sunday

The Fulfillment of Creation

Always you have been told that work is a curse and labor a misfortune.

But I say to you that when you work you fulfill a part of earth's furthest dream, assigned to you when that dream was born,

And in keeping yourself with labor you are in truth loving life,

And to love life through labor is to be intimate with life's inmost secret.

The *week of* October 29th *to* November 4th

Monday

Tuesday

Wednesday

The week of October 29th to November 4th

Thursday

Friday

The week of October 29th *to* November 4th

Saturday

Sunday

A Sense of Proportion

Said a hunted fox followed by twenty horsemen and a pack of twenty hounds, "Of course they will kill me. But how poor and how stupid they must be. Surely it would not be worthwhile for twenty foxes riding on twenty asses and accompanied by twenty wolves to chase and kill one man."

The *week of* November 5th *to* November 11th

Monday

Tuesday

Wednesday

The week of November 5th *to* November 11th

Thursday

Friday

The week of November 5th *to* November 11th

Saturday

Sunday

Fantasy and Truth

Wisdom summons us to her board that we may enjoy her food and drink; and we go thence and fill our bellies, and that table becomes an occasion for littleness and a place of self-abasement.

Nature stretches forth to us the hand of friendship and bids us take delight in her beauty; but we fear her stillness and take refuge in the city and tumble one upon another as a flock of sheep before the prowling wolf.

Truth visits us led by the smile of a child and a lover's kiss, and we close the door of our tenderness against her and abandon her as one unclean.

The human heart asks succor of us, and the spirit calls us, but we stand as one turned to stone, hearing not nor understanding.

And when one hears the cry of his heart and the call of his spirit, we say that such a one is possessed of a madness, and we cleanse ourselves of him.

The *week of* November 12th *to* November 18th

Monday

Tuesday

Wednesday

Thursday

Friday

The week of November 12th *to* November 18th

aturday

unday

Seeing the Good in Every Man

Find out the best in a person and tell him about it. We all need that. I have grown up on praise—and it has made me humble. It will always make a person long to deserve the praise. And any real consciousness is aware of something much greater than itself. Praise means understanding. We all *are* fine and great, fundamentally; overestimation of one another is impossible. Learn to see the greatness and the loveliness in one another—and to tell one another of it when we see it.

The week of November 19th *to* November 25th

Monday

Tuesday

Wednesday

The *week of* November 19th *to* November 25th

aturday

Sunday

The *week of* November 26th *to* December 2nd

Monday

Tuesday

Wednesday

The week of November 26th *to* December 2nd

Thursday

Friday

Saturday

Sunday

War and the Small Nations

Once, high above a pasture, where a sheep and a lamb were grazing, an eagle was circling and gazing hungrily down upon the lamb. And as he was about to descend and seize his prey, another eagle appeared and hovered above the sheep and her young with the same hungry intent. Then the two rivals began to fight, filling the sky with their fierce cries.

The sheep looked up and was much astonished. She turned to the lamb and said, "How strange, my child, that these two noble birds should attack one another. Is not the vast sky large enough for both of them? Pray, my little one, pray in your heart that God may make peace between your winged brothers."

And the lamb prayed in his heart.

The *week of* December 3rd *to* December 9th

Monday

Tuesday

Wednesday

Thursday

Friday

Saturday

Sunday

The Shadows of Reality

The many books and the strange patterns and beautiful thoughts are the shades of those spirits that came ere you were come. The words that you do weave are a bond between you and your brothers. The conclusions, grievous and joyous, are the seeds that the past did scatter in the field of the spirit to be reaped by the future. That youth who plays with your desires is he who will open the door of your heart to let enter the light. This earth with the ever-open mouth is the savior of your spirit from the body's slavery. This world which walks with you is your heart; and your heart is all that you think that world. This creature whom you see as ignorant and small is the same who has come from God's side to learn pity through sadness, and knowledge by way of darkness.

The week of December 10th to December 16th

Monday

Tuesday

Wednesday

The *week of* December 10th *to* December 16th

Thursday

Friday

Saturday

Sunday

⊰ The Sleep-Walkers ⊱

In the town where I was born lived a woman and her daughter, who walked in their sleep.

One night, while silence enfolded the world, the woman and her daughter, walking, yet asleep, met in their mist-veiled garden.

And the mother spoke, and she said: "At last, at last, my enemy! You by whom my youth was destroyed—who have built up your life upon the ruins of mine! Would I could kill you!"

And the daughter spoke, and she said: "O hateful woman, selfish and old! Who stand between my freer self and me! Who would have my life an echo of your own faded life! Would you were dead!"

The *week of* December 17th *to* December 23rd

Monday

Tuesday

Wednesday

Thursday

Friday

The week of December 17th *to* December 23rd

Saturday

Sunday

Charity

It is well to give when asked, but it is better to give un-
asked, through understanding;
And to the open-handed the search for one who shall
receive is joy greater than giving.
And is there aught you would withhold?
All you have shall someday be given.

The *week of* December 24th *to* December 30th

Monday

Tuesday

Wednesday

The week of December 24th *to* December 30th

Thursday

Friday

Saturday

Sunday

You Are What You Do

Who can separate his faith from his actions, or his belief from his occupations?

Who can spread his hours before him, saying, "This for God and this for myself; This for my soul, and this other for my body"?

Monday

Tuesday

Wednesday

The *week of* December 31st *to* January 6th

Thursday

Friday

The *week of* December 31st *to* January 6th

Saturday

Sunday

A Note on the Type

The text of this book has been set on the Monotype in a type face named Bembo. The roman is a copy of a letter cut for the celebrated Venetian printer Aldus Manutius by Francesco Griffo, and first used in Cardinal Bembo's *De Aetna* of 1495—hence the name of the revival. Griffo's type is now generally recognized, thanks to the researches of Mr. Stanley Morison, to be the first of the old face group of types. The companion italic is an adaptation of a chancery script type designed by the Roman calligrapher and printer Lodovico degli Arrighi, called Vincentino, and used by him during the 1520's.

The book was printed by Halliday Lithograph Corp., West Hanover, Mass., and bound by The Colonial Press, Inc., Clinton, Mass. Typography and binding design by CLINT ANGLIN.